Dear Diane

This is to record
your innermost thoughts!
+ write your poetry

lots of love
Clare

Somebody once said that a dog looked up to a man as its superior, that a horse regarded a man as its equal, and that a cat looked down on him as its inferior.

– COMPTON MACKENZIE
*Scottish writer,
author of 'Whisky Galore'*

Published in Great Britain in 1985 by Exley Publications Ltd,
16 Chalk Hill, Watford, Herts WD1 4BN, United Kingdom.
Reprinted June 1988

Copyright © Running Press, 1983
This British edition © Exley Publications, 1985
ISBN 1-85015-037-0

Illustrations by Marie Garafino; edited by Helen Exley.
Printed and bound in Hungary.

The Cat Notebook

Exley Publications

Purring would seem to be, in her case, an automatic safety-valve device for dealing with happiness overflow.

– MONICA EDWARDS

A kitten is more amusing than half the people one is obliged to live with.

– LADY SYDNEY MORGAN
Irish novelist

We got her a scratch pad but she likes the chair better.
– ALASTAIR GOODMAN, 9

You don't train cats. They train you.

– ALLEN *and* IVY DODD
American writers

Even overweight cats instinctively know the cardinal rule: when fat, arrange yourself in slim poses.

– JOHN WEITZ
American clothes designer

A dog is a dog, a bird is a bird,
and a cat is a person.

– MUGSY PEABODY

*Everything a cat is and does physically is to me beautiful, lovely,
stimulating, soothing, attractive and an enchantment.*

– PAUL GALLICO
in 'Honourable Cat'

A cat is silk, steel, topaz, silver wire.
A cat is elegance, beauty, speed.
A cat eats tomtits under your bed.

– A. P. REILLY
Humorist

Cats could have ruled the Universe,
but couldn't be bothered.

– PAUL GRAY
Author and poet

Just when you are certain the foxes have got her this time, an infinitely soft, infinitely delicate touch at your ankles reassures you that she's not only alive, but has probably been spending the evening very comfortably, thank you.

– CHARLOTTE EVERSDEN
Writer and humorist

It is hard to watch natural history TV programmes with a small cat attempting to catch the flamingoes.

– WILLIAM TOMS
Author

Cat food manufacturers haven't yet cottoned on to the fact that what cats really like is bolognaise sauce, cheese, ice cream, potato crisps and anything Cordon Bleu.

– PETER DELANEY
Writer and poet

*About a year ago I won some goldfish at a fair,
but guess who ate them!*

– LOUISE ALLISON, *10*

All over the world there are intelligent adult human beings on their hands and knees trying to show a cat where the tit-bit they threw has landed.

– MARCIA FISCHER
Writer

The greater cats with golden eyes
Stare out between the bars.
Deserts are there, and different skies,
And night with different stars.

– V. SACKVILLE-WEST
British poet, novelist and horticulturist

Whatever you have opened — box, cupboard, chest, sideboard, wardrobe, car boot, trunk or music stool — check before you shut it. There's probably a cat inside.

– VICKI KNOWLES
Author

Only cat lovers know the luxury of fur-coated,
musical hot water bottles that never go cold.

– SUSANNE MILLEN
Writer

It may not be hygienic, but it's very touching to go in to kiss your sleeping child goodnight and find two heads on the pillow.

– PATTY GARNHAM
Writer

After scolding one's cat one looks into its face and is seized by the ugly suspicion that it understood every word. And his filed it for reference.

– PAM BROWN
Writer and poet,
author of 'Mutterings of a Char'

*Cats have an infallible understanding of total concentration
– and get between you and it.*

– ARTHUR BRIDGES
Writer and humorist

Cats were put into the world to disprove the dogma that all things were created to serve man.

– PAUL GRAY
Author and poet

As to sagacity, I should say that his judgment respecting the warmest place and the softest cushion in a room is infallible, his punctuality at meal times is admirable, and his pertinacity in jumping on people's shoulders till they give him some of the best of what is going, indicates great firmness.

– THOMAS HENRY HUXLEY
19th century English biologist

Cat said 'I am not a friend, and I am not a servant. I am the Cat who walks by himself, and I wish to come into your Cave.'

– RUDYARD KIPLING
Just So Stories

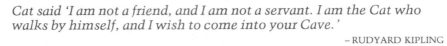

Every cat has a sure-fire method of getting your attention – this can range from deep-throated curses to high, desperate wailings, from tearing at the carpets to hammering at the pane, from poking you in the eye with a stick-like paw to persistently covering your face with tiny lickings, from gnawing your ear to running up your back.

You soon learn it's better to comply.

– ALAN CHAPMAN
Author

[Cats] cannot, like obstinate children, be persuaded or forced to do anything, even for their own good.

– SHORT STORIES, OR, TREASURES OF TRUTH
1830 book for children

There is nothing better after a long, wet, dismal walk home than a small cat trotting fast to meet you, tail up and pink mouth open in indignation.

– ANTOINETTE MAYER
Author

Given a houseful of carpets, shelves, cushions, chairs, window sills, any cat will choose to sleep on the document you are using.

– DOMINIC COURCEL
English-born author

A cat thinks in cat terms—a million years of domestication have not turned it into a pseudo-human and a million more probably won't, either.

– ALLEN *and* IVY DODD
American writers

Her function is to sit and be admired.
— GEORGINA STRICKLAND GATES

The real objection to the great majority of cats is their insufferable air of superiority.

– P. G. WODEHOUSE
English humorist
creator of 'Jeeves'

Cats have a contempt of speech. Why should they talk
when they can communicate without words?
                                    – LILIAN JACKSON BRAUN
                                        American writer

One small cat changes coming home to an empty house to coming home.

– LUCY WHEELER
Author and poet

Stately, kindly, lordly friend condescend
Here to sit by me, and turn
Glorious eyes that smile and burn. . . .

– ALGERNON CHARLES SWINBURNE
Late 19th century English poet
and dramatist

Once you have been presented with a mouse by your cat, you will never be the same again. She can use you for a door-mat. And she will too.

– PAUL GALLICO
in 'My Boss The Cat'

The cat is domestic only as far as suits its own ends; it will not be kennelled or harnessed nor suffer any dictation as to its goings-out or comings-in.

– SAKI [Hector Hugh Munro]
English short-story writer

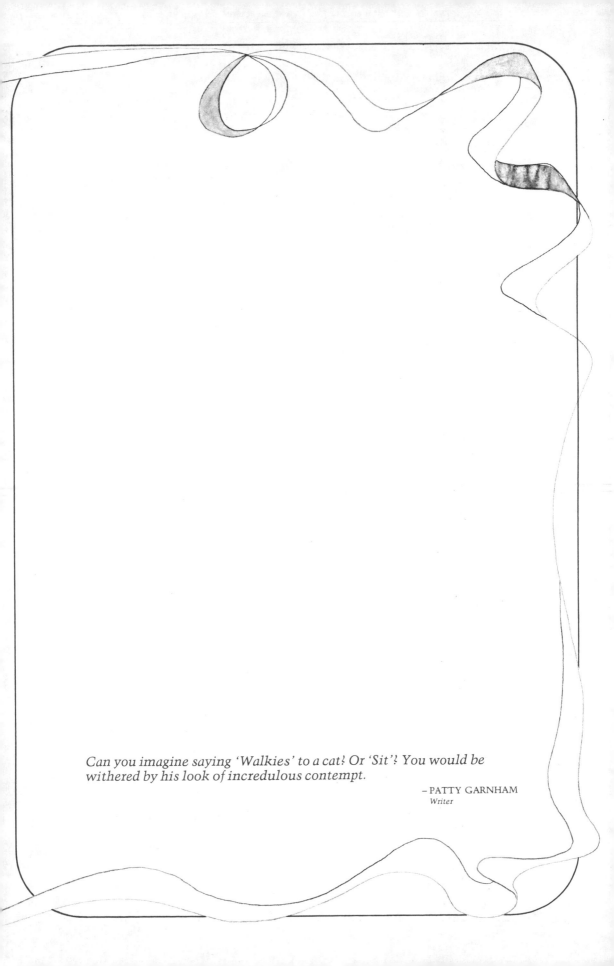

Can you imagine saying 'Walkies' to a cat? Or 'Sit'? You would be withered by his look of incredulous contempt.

– PATTY GARNHAM
Writer

It is impossible for a lover of cats to banish these alert, gentle and discriminating little friends, who give us just enough of their regard and complaisance to make us hunger for more.

– AGNES REPPLIER
Essayist

There are no ordinary cats.
– COLETTE
French writer,
author of 'Gigi'.

Cats can work out mathematically the exact place to sit that will cause the most inconvenience.

– MICHAEL STEVENS
Writer and humorist

It is remarkable, in cats, that the outer life they reveal to their masters is one of perpetual confident boredom.

– ROBLEY WILSON JR.

If you have a cat you need a remote control to your television. And a butler. There is no huff like the huff of a cat who has chosen his knee for the evening and finds himself forcibly evicted.

– DENISE HAWKINS
Author

Cats are kindly masters, just so long as you remember your place.

– PAUL GRAY
Author and poet

His friendship is not easily won
but it is something worth having.

– MICHAEL JOSEPH
English publisher

I love in the cat that independent and most ungrateful temper which prevents it from attaching itself to anyone; the indifference with which it passes from the salon to the housetop.

– FRANCOIS RENE DE CHATEAUBRIAND
Early 19th century French novelist,
poet and politician

A cat is a lion in a jungle of small bushes.
— INDIAN PROVERB

Sometimes the veil between human and animal intelligence wears very thin—then one experiences the supreme thrill of keeping a cat, or perhaps allowing oneself to be owned by a cat.

– CATHERINE MANLEY
18th century English writer

If it's raining at the back door every cat is convinced there's a good chance that it won't be raining at the front door.

– WILLIAM TOMS
Author

Once it has given its love, what absolute confidence, what fidelity of affection! It will make itself the companion of your hours of work, of loneliness, or of sadness. It will lie the whole evening on your knee, purring and happy in your society, and leaving the company of creatures of its own society to be with you.

– THEOPHILE GAUTIER
*19th century French poet
and novelist*

In Ancient Egypt they were worshipped as gods. This makes them too prone to set themselves up as critics and censors of the frail and erring human beings whose lot they share.

– P. G. WODEHOUSE
English humorist,
creator of 'Jeeves'

*Out-thinking a cat that doesn't much want to come in,
is a refinement of chess.*

– DOMINIC COURCEL
English-born author

A little drowsing cat is an image of perfect beatitude.
– CHAMPFLEURY [Jules Fleury-Husson]
19th century French writer

Sam raised his paw for all the world as if he were about to protest, and then, apparently thinking better of it, he pretended instead that the action had been only for the purpose of commencing his nightly wash.

– WALTER DE LA MARE
English poet and author,
writer of children's verse

A cat is never bored. At a loose end he will remove all the drawing pins from the walls, or the keys from their hooks, climb the north face of the bookcase or eat the rubber plant. Or retire to the bath to catch spiders. Or tear the lavatory roll into shreds. Or simply go out and catch something. Large.

– ROBERT JAMES
Writer

A cat will imagine a piece of paper on a string to be a mouse, until you enter into the spirit of the game. It will then regard you as a lunatic and take to washing its feet.

– PAM BROWN
Writer and poet
Author of 'Mutterings of a Char'

Doctors have just discovered the therapeutic value of possessing and fondling a cat. Which anyone who has lived with a cat could have told them over the last six thousand years or more.

– ANNE TAYLOR-BROWNE
Writer and poet

No heaven will not ever Heaven be
Unless my cats are there to welcome me.
– EPITAPH IN A PET CEMETERY

The really great thing about cats is their endless variety. One can pick a cat to fit almost any kind of decor, colour scheme, income, personality, mood. But under the fur, whatever colour it may be, there still lies, essentially unchanged, one of the world's free souls.

– ERIC GURNEY
Cartoonist and writer

*A cat sees no good reason why it should obey another animal,
even if it does stand on two legs.*

– SARAH THOMPSON
Writer

You only realise too late why the cat was on top of the fridge when you notice how smooth *the butter is.*

– PETER DELANEY
Writer and poet

Everybody loves him, and he, perfectly amicably,
loves nothing except himself.

– MELISSA JONES, *12*

A kitten is the most irresistible comedian in the world. Its wide-open eyes gleam with wonder and mirth. It darts madly at nothing at all, and then, as though suddenly checked in the pursuit, prances sideways on its hind legs with ridiculous agility and zeal.

– AGNES REPPLIER
Essayist

A cat is a Regency gentleman – elegant of pose, exquisite of manner,
with spotless linen and an enthusiasm for bare knuckle fights,
rampaging love affairs, duels by moonlight and the singing of glees.
He expects immaculate service from his domestic staff, and possesses
a range of invective that would make a navvy blanch.

– PAM BROWN
Writer and poet,
author of 'Mutterings of a Char'

Ignorant people think it's the noise which fighting cats make that is so aggravating, but it ain't so, it's the sickening grammar they use.

– MARK TWAIN
19th century humorist,
author of 'Huckleberry Finn'

Cats like to eat cacti, teazles, brooms, aluminium foil and string.
They need every life they've got.

– WILLIAM TOMS
Author

Cats can be very funny, and have the oddest ways of showing they're glad to see you. Rudimace always peed in our shoes.

– W. H. AUDEN
English-born poet and essayist

*No matter how tired or wretched I am, a pussy-cat sitting
in a doorway can divert my mind.*

– MARY E. WILKINS

Cats know how to obtain food without labour, shelter without confinement and love without penalties.

— W. L. GEORGE

Screeching, yowling that's what it's like to humans.
To the cat it's like Handel, Bach or Schuman.

– ANNE-MARIE HAWKES, *11*

A drowsy winter evening is never quite drowsy enough without a sleeping cat.

– DENISE HAWKINS
Author

A cat isn't fussy – just so long as you remember he likes his milk in the shallow, rose-patterned saucer and his fish on the blue plate. From which he will take it, and eat it off the floor.

– ARTHUR BRIDGES
Writer and humorist

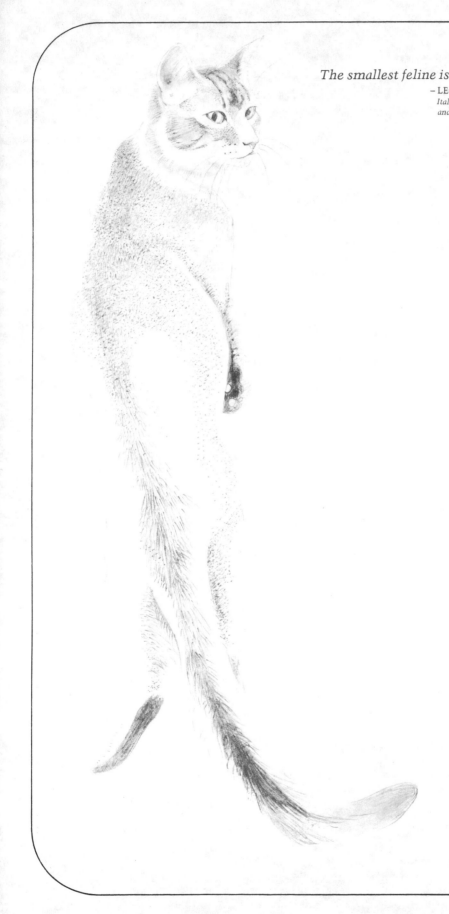

The smallest feline is a masterpiece.
– LEONARDO DA VINCI
*Italian Renaissance artist
and scientist*

A kitten is so flexible that she is almost double; the hind parts are equivalent to another kitten with which the forepart plays. She does not discover that her tail belongs to her until you tread on it.

– HENRY DAVID THOREAU
19th century American writer, author of 'Walden'

You can tell a dog to do something. You can put it to a cat as a reasonable proposition.

– MICHAEL STEVENS
Writer and humorist

Cats feel that they can offer useful advice and a serviceable paw in almost any task you have in hand. All cats help type, write letters, dust, make beds and garden. Some feel you also need help in the bath. The more insane like hoovering and hot irons.

– CHARLOTTE EVERSDEN
Writer and humorist

Perhaps a child, like a cat, is so much inside himself
that he does not see himself in the mirror.

– ANAÏS NIN
American diarist

When a cat is offended every square centimetre of him is offended. Men and women of power and intellect have been brought to their knees by cats who have turned their backs on them.

– A. P. REILLY
Humorist

If a cat has decided to love you, there's not a great deal you can do about it.

– KATRINA SMYTHE
Author

If you want to be a psychological novelist and write about human beings, the best thing you can do is keep a pair of cats.

– ALDOUS HUXLEY
*English novelist,
author of 'Brave New World'*

You can feel an awful fool standing at the bottom of the garden yelling pussy, pussy, pussy across a totally deserted meadow. Especially when you realise that pussy, pussy, pussy is watching you, with benign interest, from the shelter of the garden shed.

– MARCIA FISCHER
Writer

The cat who loves you only knows he wants to be curled round your shoulders – and pitons up your spine are one way to get there. The other way is to drop on you from a great height.

– MICHAEL STEVENS
Writer and humorist

There are people who reshape the world by force or argument, but the cat just lies there, dozing, and the world quietly reshapes itself to suit his comfort and convenience.

– ALLEN *and* IVY DODD
American writers

*The cat is the only animal which accepts the comforts
but rejects the bondage of domesticity.*
– GEORGES LOUIS LECLERC DE BUFFON
18th century French naturalist

The cat, like the genius, draws into itself as into a shell except in the atmosphere of congeniality, and this is the secret of its remarkable and elusive personality.

– IDA M. MELLEN

The tail, in cats, is the principal organ of emotional expression, and a Manx cat is the equivalent of a dumb man.

*English novelist,
author of 'Brave New World'*

A dog is like a liberal. He wants to please everybody. A cat really doesn't need to know that everybody loves him.

– WILLIAM KUNSTLER

Give her but a wavering leaf-shadow of a breeze combing the grasses and she was back a million years, glaring with night-lit eyes in the thickets, projecting a terrible aura of fear that stilled and quelled all creatures.

– PAUL ANNIXTER

CAT: A pygmy lion who loves mice, hates dogs, and patronises human beings.

– OLIVER HERFORD
English writer and illustrator

Four little Persians, but one only looked in my direction. I extended a tentative finger and two soft paws clung to it. There was a contented sound of purring. I suspect on both our parts.

– GEORGE FREEDLEY

There is nothing so lowering to one's self-esteem as the affectionate contempt of a beloved cat.

– AGNES REPPLIER
Essayist

Cats allow us to love them, for which we should be duly grateful.

– ANNE TAYLOR-BROWNE
Writer and poet

Cats bring you prezzies. The worst is the row of bodiless mouse faces beside the milk bottle.

— KATRINA SMYTHE
Author

Cats do not wear their hearts on their sleeves, which is not to say they do not miss you when you are away.

However, they feel that you have behaved very badly, and may not be very civil when you return. After you have apologised, normal relations can be resumed.

– SUSANNE MILLEN
Writer

A cat is beautiful at a distance – near-to he is an inexhaustible matter for wonder: the patterning of his eyes, the elaborations of his ears, the beautiful precision of his nostril, the elaborate whorls of his face fur, the elegance of his bones, the delicacy of his sinews, the efficiency of his paws, the separate aliveness of his tail. His mouth is incredibly clean, incredibly pink. His teeth are precision made. The roof is rippled, his tongue rasped. Everything he does is a perfection. He does, however, not wish it to be recorded for posterity. Try to draw him and he will at once shift his position – or stare at one in a huff. His beauty is a private matter.

– PAM BROWN
Writer and poet ,
author of 'Mutterings of a Char'